POETRY BOOK 1

Annie Can Whistle and Other Poems

ANNIE CAN WHISTLE

Written by **Mary Dodson Wade**

Illustrated by **Guy Francis**

Annie can whistle.
Make her lips round,
blow right through,
make that sound
that I couldn't do.

I tried.
No luck.
That worrisome whistle
just stayed stuck.

I tried again,
and soft and thin,
the whistle got free,
wonderful whistle
from inside of me.

Whirl around!
Make that sound.
Sparkling, sunny note,
shrill and high.
Annie can whistle,
   and
      so
         can
            I.

DINNERTIME

Written by **Wynelle Ririe**

Illustrated by **Suzanne Smith**

Down by the bogs, where it's wet and gray,

Many creatures come to play.

Something is waiting, strong and green.

Where could it be? Can it be seen?

Its leaves have teeth! They look like knives!

The small white flowers look like eyes!

Beetles, bugs, flies, and more—

Venus's flytrap is an insectivore!

The leaves, they sparkle, wet and sweet.

Fly buzzes by and says, "What a treat!"

Fly lands on one leaf, smooth and thick.

Fly bows its head and takes a lick.

Cool, sweet juice on a summer day

Tastes so good . . . Fly wants to stay.

"Just a few more licks," it says with glee.

Venus's flytrap is pleased as can be.

Little leaf-hairs tickle Fly—

It's too busy to ask why.

The leaf snaps shut. Its pointed spines

Trap silly Fly—it's dinnertime!

LITTLE WHITE PONY

Adapted and translated by **Karen Sharp Foster**

Illustrated by **Hala Day**

Little white pony,
take me far away.
Take me to my hometown.
That's where I will stay.

I have, I have, I have—
I have a little farm.
I have three sheep waiting
in a little barn.

One sheep gives me milk,
another gives me wool,
another gives me butter,
and for the week, I'm full.

CABALLITO BLANCO

Caballito blanco,
llévame de aquí.
Llévame a mi pueblo
donde yo nací.

Tengo, tengo, tengo —
tengo una granja.
Tengo tres ovejas
en una cabaña.

Una me da leche,
otra me da lana,
otra mantequilla
para la semana.

I SEE GREEN

Written by **Nyman Brooks**

Illustrated by **Margaret Willis**

When I lie on my stomach and look at the grass, I see green.

But then I look closer.

I see each grass blade.

Some point crisply green. Some are blue.

Some wilt yellow and flat.

Then I look closer.

I see tan moths.

They fold their wings like closed umbrellas.

They fly up when I brush my hand over the lawn.

Then I look closer.

I see a leaf hopper, hard as a seed, stiff as a spring.

Suddenly he disappears.

Then I look closer.

I see a root-beer colored ant.

I see a sow bug, like a tiny armadillo.

I see a mite, a pin-prick of red.

Then I look closer.

I see a whole world,

A tiny forest appearing and disappearing,

Full of living things, coming and going.

I push my finger down and feel the cool, moist earth.

Then I roll on my back and look up into the sky.

CLOWNS IN THE CAR

Written by **Mary Dodson Wade**

Illustrated by **Brenden Taylor**

Here come the clowns
In a funny, old car.
You can't guess
How many there are.

One comes out,
Then two, then four.
You think they're through,
And then come more.

It's a mystery to me,
The biggest by far,
How they get so many
In that little, old car.

SPARKLES

Written by **Mary Dodson Wade**

Illustrated by **Bruce Martin**

Light has colors—
it's strange to say,
but I know it's true.
I saw them today.
A halo of colors,
   red and blue,
      from a glass of water
         the sun shone through.

My mother's ring
can make light dance,
an explosion of color
   quite
      by
         chance.

The sky isn't blue—
it just looks that way.
My sweater is red
during the day.
But when night smothers light,
my sweater in the chair
    becomes a black cat
        puddled
           there.

Light has colors—
it's strange to say.
And who keeps colors
safe at night,
waiting to sparkle
    in
        bright
           sunlight?